The Roof Garden

Written by Bronwyn Tainui

Illustrated by Simon Barr and M Makatoa

Jessie lived with her grandpa, Pop. They lived in an apartment. There was no garden, so Pop grew plants in pots on the rooftop. He liked to grow fruit and vegetables. He took care of his plants and watered them every day.

One day, Pop fell and broke his hip. Then, he had surgery to have his hip replaced.

Pop was still getting better, so he couldn't walk very well. "You will have to look after our plants, otherwise they won't grow properly," he said to Jessie.

At first, Jessie didn't answer. She wasn't sure she could look after the plants. However, she liked spending time on the rooftop. "OK, Pop," she said. "No problem."

On Monday, Pop said, "The weather's been just right for tomatoes, so ours should be ripe. Would you pick some for dinner, Jess?"

Jessie picked some small, green tomatoes from the pots by the shady wall. They did not look like last year's fat, red tomatoes.

Jessie gave Pop the tomatoes.

"Oh dear," said Pop. "These tomatoes are still tiny and green. That means they haven't been getting enough sunlight. Didn't I put them in the sun?"

"Sorry, Pop," said Jessie. "Because I needed more room to bounce my basketball, I moved some of the plants against the shady wall."

"Why do plants need the sun?" Jessie asked.

"The leaves of a plant take in energy from the sun. The energy helps the plant make sugar. As a result, the plant can grow. We eat the plant, so it gives us energy, too," answered Pop.

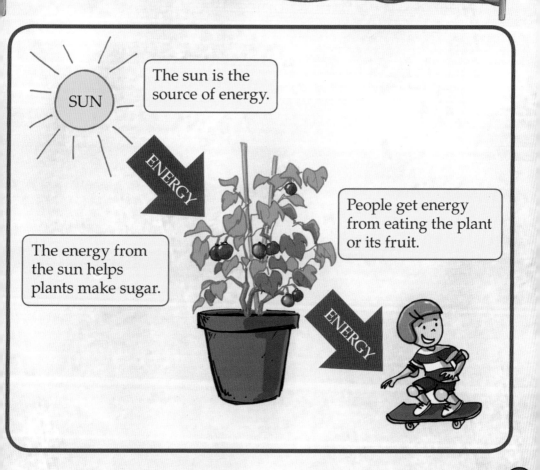

The sun is the source of energy.

The energy from the sun helps plants make sugar.

People get energy from eating the plant or its fruit.

On Tuesday, Pop said, "We've had a lot of sun, so the strawberries should be ripe. Could you please pick some to have for dessert, Jess?"

Jessie picked strawberries off the strawberry plants that sat in a long box against the wall. Last year's strawberries had been fat and juicy. But these ones were full of holes, because Jessie hadn't noticed the birds sneakily eating them.

"Oh, no!" said Pop when he saw the strawberries. "I think you forgot to put the net over them! That's why they are bird-pecked."

On Wednesday, Pop said, "Our beans should be ready. Pick me some beans please, Jess."

But the bean plants were wilted. Jessie thought they must be dying. She pulled off some bean pods. They were very dry. Jessie had almost killed Pop's bean plants, because she'd left them in the sun and only watered them once during the week.

Jessie gave the bean pods to Pop.

"Didn't you water these, Jess?" asked Pop.

"Sorry, Pop. I didn't know they needed water every day," said Jessie. "How do plants drink the water, anyway?"

"The roots take in nutrients and water from the soil. Then, the nutrients and water travel up the plant's stems to the leaves, so the plant can make fruit," answered Pop.

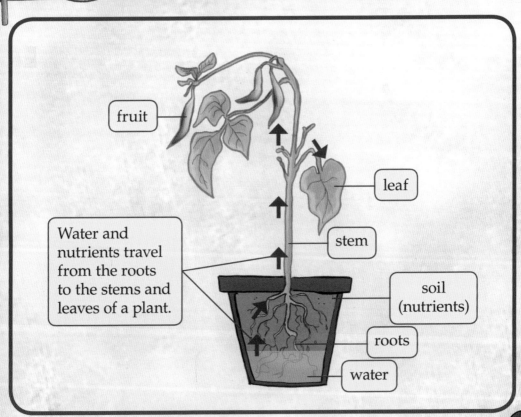

fruit

leaf

Water and nutrients travel from the roots to the stems and leaves of a plant.

stem

soil (nutrients)

roots

water

"How do you make your fruit and vegetables grow so well, Pop?" asked Jessie.

"As well as sun and water, having good, rich soil is important," Pop replied.

"Really?" asked Jessie.

"Yes," answered Pop. "There are living things in soil, too. Some are big, such as worms. Some are tiny and we can't see them. They feed on the remains of dead insects and rotting plants in the soil. This breaks down the material and makes the soil rich."

Pop continued, "Plants that grow in pots need more care, because they haven't got much soil to get nutrients and water from."

"I'm sorry I let you down, Pop," said Jessie.

"You know what?" answered Pop, "I should have been a lot more helpful. I just thought you'd know what to do, like me. But I only know what to do because I've been gardening for years."

"That's OK, Pop," said Jessie, smiling. "I have a great idea for your garden. Worms! Let's build a worm farm. Then, the worms will help make the soil rich. We can work on it together."

Pop grinned. "I always knew you were a gardener at heart, Jess."